ESCAPE ROOM

CAN YOU ESCAPE THE VIDEO GAME?

DR GARETH MOORE

ILLUSTRATED BY DGPH STUDIO

WELBECK

THIS IS A WELBECK CHILDREN'S BOOK

Published in 2021 by Welbeck Children's Books,
an imprint of Welbeck Children's Limited,
part of Welbeck Publishing Group,
20 Mortimer Street, London W1T 3JW.

A CIP catalogue record for this book is available from the British Library.

ISBN: 978-1-78312-642-2

Printed in China

10 9 8 7 6 5 4 3 2 1

Story, text, puzzles and models written and designed by Dr Gareth Moore
Commissioning Editor: Bryony Davies
Story Editor: Joff Brown
Managing Art Editor: Matt Drew
Production: Melanie Robertson

HOW TO PLAY

ARE YOU READY TO ESCAPE THE VIDEO GAME?

In a moment you'll turn the page to begin your adventure,
but first, here's how to play...

As you follow the story through the book, you'll meet a series of mind-boggling puzzles. To solve each one, you'll need to use pressed-out items from the card sheets in the envelope inside the book. It's your job to work out which item you need for each puzzle.

If you get stuck, look at the pressed-out hint card for that puzzle (see below). There are three hints on each card. Turn the hint card around to read hint 1, which is on the back, and see if you can now solve the puzzle. If not, flip the card over to look at hint 2, and then, if you need to, turn it again to read hint 3. You can check your answers on page 48. Good luck!

Before you begin, take everything out of the envelope inside the book:

1. Find the four hint card sheets. Press out the cards and fold each one along the crease so that you see the front. Put them to one side as you play. Make sure you can't see the back of each card!

2. The rest of the sheets contain items that you will use to solve the puzzles. Press them out as you make your way through the book. You'll need to fold some of them to make 3D objects:

- Press them out carefully, pushing out any sections that have diagonal lines on them.

- Then fold them along the creases – with the dotted lines facing you, fold away from you.

Press out & fold!

- Push the tabs into the slots to hold them together. The tabs and slots are labelled with letters to help you push the correct tabs into the correct slots – start with A and continue in alphabetical order.

- **Don't use tape – if you do, you won't be able to unfold and reuse the items.**

3. When you've finished playing, keep all your items safe in the envelope.

Press out & build!

THE NEW GAME

Where did this game disc come from? It's been left on top of the console in your living room. What kind of game tells you NOT to play it? This could be fun...

You insert the disc into the machine. As the game starts up, the TV screen starts shimmering and rippling like water. You feel a strange, unstoppable pull. Before you know it, you're hurtling towards the TV screen... and then you pass right through it.

You find yourself zooming through a vortex of glowing pixels. Behind you, the tiny rectangle of the TV screen disappears into the distance. You're trapped inside the game!

Curse of the Dragon

WARNING

DO NOT PLAY!

You come to a stop in front of an enormous wall of words. This must be a level-select screen. If you can make it through all six levels... perhaps you can escape the game?

LEVEL SELECT

LEVEL 1
A-MAZE-O-TRON
8

LEVEL 2
CLOUDLAND CAPERS
14

LEVEL 3
TEMPLE OF TERROR
20

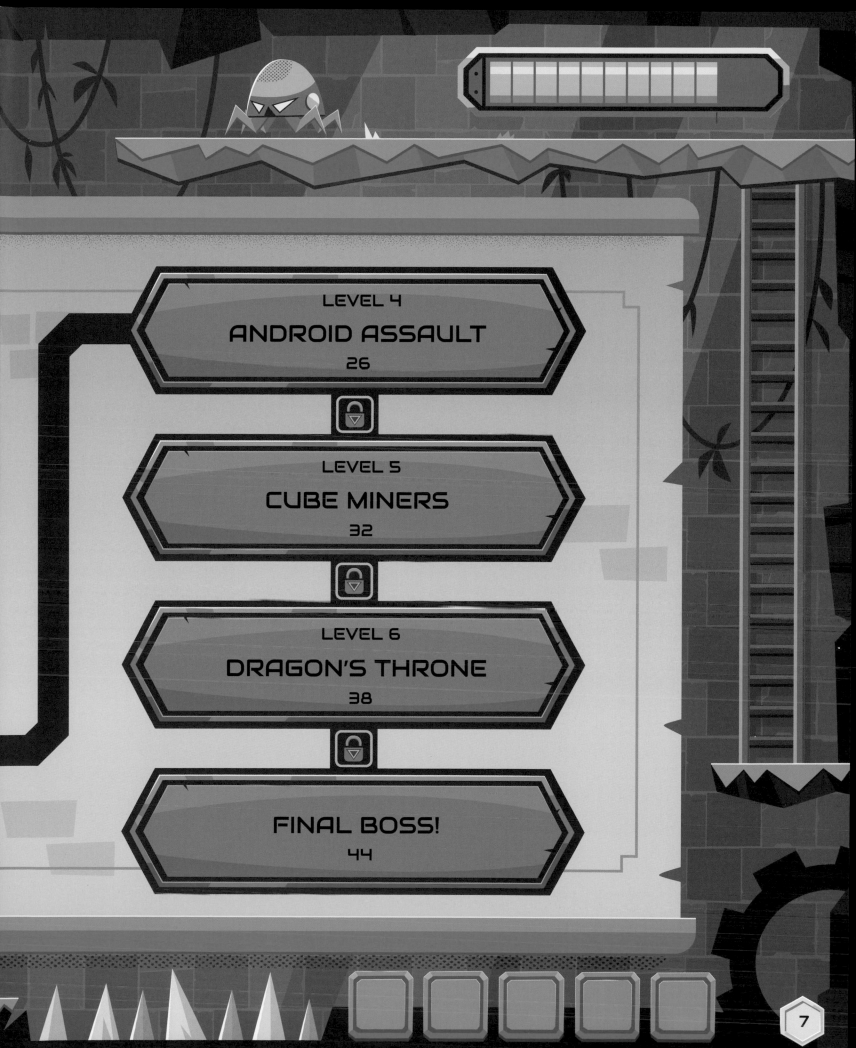

LEVEL 4

ANDROID ASSAULT

26

LEVEL 5

CUBE MINERS

32

LEVEL 6

DRAGON'S THRONE

38

FINAL BOSS!

44

A-MAZE-O-TRON

You select the first level – and you're instantly zapped into a very strange place. It's a vast maze, filled with roaming monsters, secret passages and power-ups.

Text appears in front of you, with a small image of a dragon beneath it:

SOLVE THE PUZZLES TO ESCAPE THE LEVEL!

What puzzles? You look around. There must be more to this maze than meets the eye. If you can dodge the monsters and search for clues, you might just make it out of here...

In front of you, a **SMALL MAZE** pops up, blocking your way. Can you find your way across? Drop the **GREEN JIGSAW PIECES** into the grid to mark out a route from the entrance to the exit.

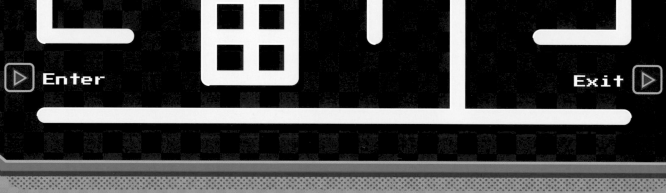

▷ Enter

Exit ▷

The exit is locked, and needs a **FOUR-DIGIT CODE** to let you through. What is the code?

STUCK?
YOUR HINT CARDS CONTAIN EXTRA CLUES TO HELP YOU FIGURE OUT THE PUZZLES.

You enter the next zone of the maze. But this doesn't make sense – there's no way to reach the exit!

And then you notice **COLUMNS OF LIGHT** ascending up to another floor. It looks like you need to **TRAVEL UP AND DOWN BETWEEN FLOORS** to complete this maze!

Find the map of the extra floor and **INSTALL IT TO COMPLETE THE MAZE**. You can only travel between floors by jumping between a number and the hole immediately above it, or vice versa.

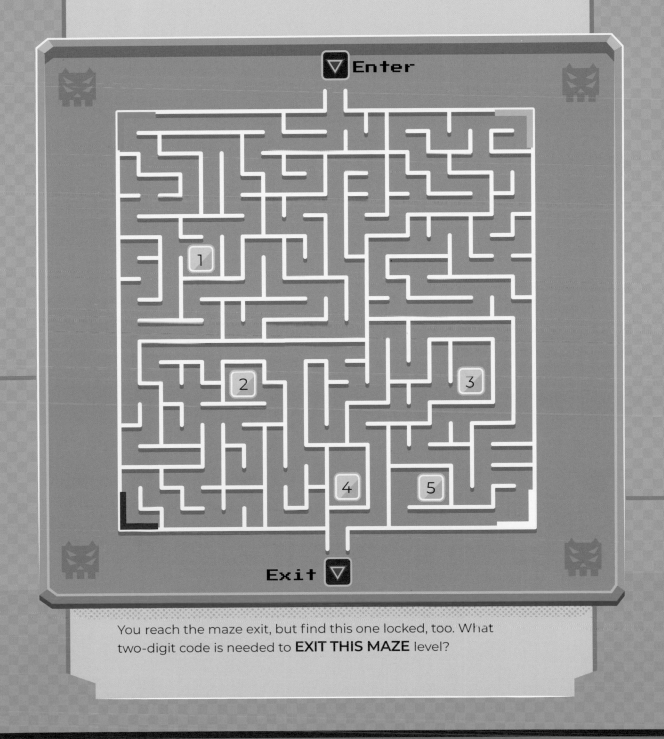

▽ Enter

Exit ▽

You reach the maze exit, but find this one locked, too. What two-digit code is needed to **EXIT THIS MAZE** level?

You find yourself looking down on the maze, in control of a **YELLOW MANIC MUNCHER PIECE**. Can you **STEER IT THROUGH THE MAZE** to the black cube without letting any of the ghosts see you? Ghosts can only see in horizontal or vertical lines, and they can't see through walls.

Use the special manic muncher piece on the yellow controllers below to **INPUT THE SEQUENCE OF CHANGES OF DIRECTION** needed to move the manic muncher through the maze to the cube. The manic muncher keeps moving the same way until you change direction.

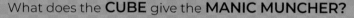

What does the **CUBE** give the **MANIC MUNCHER?**

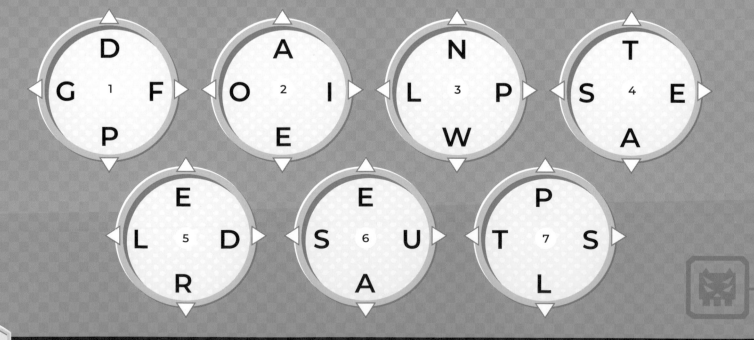

As the manic muncher reaches the cube, you find yourself suddenly shrunk inside the maze, **HOLDING THE CUBE**. But now that you have a better view of it, you realize it is itself **ANOTHER MAZE**.

Hold the cube and rotate it to find a route from '**START**' to '**EXIT**'. What is the **PASSWORD** that you need to exit this level?

CLOUDLAND CAPERS

Everything dissolves in a swirl of pixels... and suddenly you find yourself teetering on the edge of an impossibly high platform. Cute-faced clouds swirl around you. The ground below is too far away to even see.

"Hey, buddy!" squeaks a passing cloud. "If you want to escape this level, you'd better solve all the puzzles!"

You glance around, already looking for clues. There must be a way out somewhere...

"Listen!" squeaks the cloud. "To get out of the first part of the level, you can only **WALK LEFT OR RIGHT** or **CLIMB UP OR DOWN LADDERS** – and you can't jump or fall!"

Can you use the existing platforms and ladders provided to **CREATE A ROUTE** from where you enter, at the top left, to the door at the bottom left? One platform and one ladder are placed already, to show you how it works. The door will only open if you **COLLECT SIX COINS** along the way, and once you've used a platform or ladder it can't be removed, so use them wisely!

Start

Exit

You make it down the last ladder and pass through the door into a new section of the level, **FILLED WITH CHARACTERS**. Some will hurt you, but one is harmless. How do you know which is which?

Luckily you find a **MAGIC TELESCOPE** which allows you to examine the creatures from a new perspective. Can you use it to work out which two of these three creatures must be avoided?

You zip past the enemies and reach a big sign saying, "**END OF LEVEL – BOSS NEAR**". But what's this? You need to have at least 3000 points to battle the boss. Do you have a high enough score to progress?

You go to check your score, but it's not displaying. All the screen says is "**SCORE**", with a jumbled-up display below it. Can you update the display so it shows your **ACTUAL SCORE**?

You reveal your score – and it's high enough to continue and take on the end-of-level boss. You try to jump on him to win, but something's wrong. He's just a **JUMBLE OF GLITCHY PIXELS**.

Can you find **FIVE PIECES OF THE BROKEN GRAPHIC** and use them to fix the glitches on the boss, so he looks just like the one on the sign? Once he's assembled, you can defeat him and exit the level!

DANGER!

TEMPLE OF TERROR

Cloudland swirls away. You give a sigh of relief at having got away from all those high platforms – then you yelp with terror. You're on the edge of a narrow, crumbling stone ledge, high up on an ancient ruin. Far below you is a forbidding temple, half-crumbled into the precipice below.

Something is etched into the rock: "FOUR PUZZLES LIE WITHIN". Shakily, you make your way down, jumping from block to block, and you start looking for signs of ancient puzzles.

You scan the horizon, then suddenly something drops from a ledge above you and lands on your back. You shout and brush it off – it's a cheeky-looking monkey.

He jumps onto a branch and hands you a **SCRAP OF PAPER**. It's a map of the area. With a shriek he points at it and says: "Tell me **THREE HIDDEN NUMBERS**, and I'll help you read the map."

You look at your map and **FOLD IT CAREFULLY**.

Can you find the **THREE NUMBERS** hidden on the map?

You tell the monkey the numbers, and he jabs at a place on the map, then points to a **HUGE TEMPLE DOOR!** You try to open it, but it's sealed shut. You look more closely at the door. Near the top are four strangely shaped carvings, and beneath them is a **STRANGE OCTAGONAL PATTERN WITH EIGHT BUTTONS**:

The monkey bounds up with another gift – this time, it's an **EIGHT-SIDED STONE SLAB**. You place it on the pattern, and it glows four times. Can you choose which **FOUR BUTTONS TO PRESS** to unlock the door?

The door swings open, and you **ENTER THE TEMPLE ATRIUM**. It's cool and dark. In front of you is a set of double doors, held shut by a strangely modern-looking **FOUR-DIGIT LOCK**.

Carved high up above the doors is a code.

Lying on the floor are some **SMALL SCRAPS OF PARCHMENT** that have the same symbols on them that are above the door. Could these be the key to working out the four-digit code?

You open the door and enter the temple's main chamber. It's huge and echoing, with flaming torches providing warmth.

Sunlight streams through high windows on to an **ALTAR** in the middle of the chamber. The altar has **MANY LETTERS** on it.

The monkey talks again. "Speak the password to escape the level," it says, "or be lost forever!" As it talks, it frantically drags a **RAGGED ALTAR CLOTH** towards you. Could this help you discover the password?

ANDROID ASSAULT

As you utter the password, the temple vanishes and you find yourself looking out across a vast, gleaming city, with hover cars flying between tall buildings. Across the cityscape, warriors with blaster guns are fighting deadly looking robots.

"Get out of here!" a fighter yells at you. "This is a war zone! Solve the four puzzles to make your escape!"

Dodging the laser blasts, you begin your search for clues...

An explosion knocks you off your feet. "The **ANDROIDS ARE ALMOST HERE!**" the fighter says. "We need to access that elevator shaft and climb down!"

He jabs at a **FIVE-DIGIT PANEL**. "Uh... I've forgotten the code. Can you help?" All you can see are **FIVE RINGS**. Can you work out the code to access the shaft?

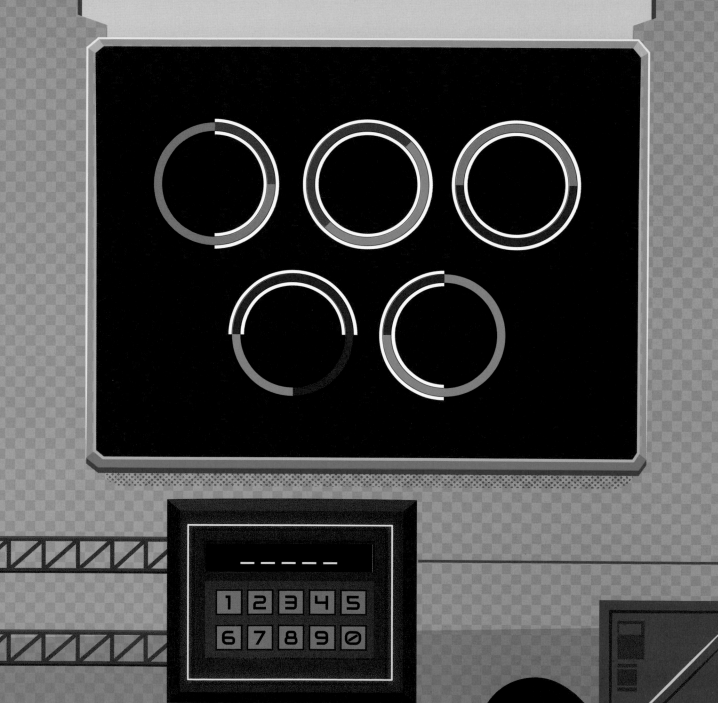

You open the elevator shaft and climb down. You hear an **OMINOUS CLANKING** and look up. One of the deadly androids is following you!

You reach the bottom of the shaft and dash out to the street. "C'mon!" yells the fighter, running to a **SLEEK-LOOKING HOVER CAR**. "Let's use this car to get out of here – quick!"

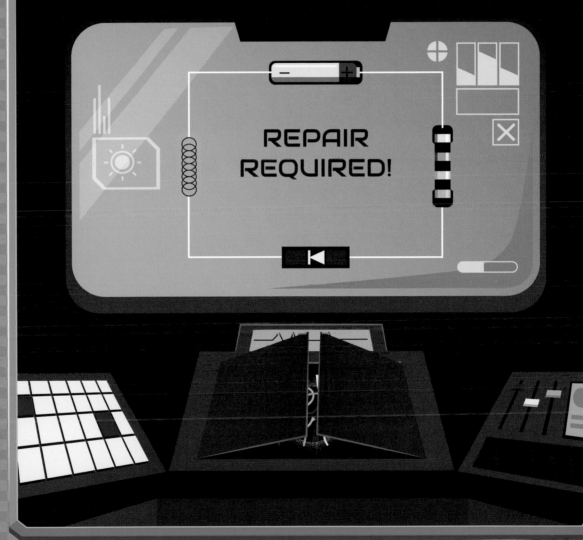

A green screen on the dashboard of the hover car is flashing up a message: "**REPAIR REQUIRED!**"

"We need to **BUILD THE CIRCUIT** to start the car," the fighter says.

When you have built the circuit, electricity travels around it from the '**+**' to the '**-**'. What **FOUR-WORD MESSAGE** does it display?

You **ZOOM OFF IN THE HOVER CAR** just as the android reaches the bottom of the shaft and runs out on to the street. The car zips through the city battlefield and **SCREECHES TO A HALT** in a quieter part of the city. You get out, and the fighter flies off.

You are on a pathway with **FOUR CIRCULAR VIEWING PLATFORMS**, each with an arrow on it. At the end of the pathway is a portal, protected by a robot. The portal needs a **FOUR-DIGIT CODE** to open.

"The four digits must be **HIDDEN SOMEWHERE AROUND HERE**," you say. What is the code? What can you see?

You enter the digits, and the portal **GLOWS WITH LIGHT**. It's your way out! You step forward – but it's a trap! The robot suddenly springs into action and **BLOCKS YOUR WAY** with lasers.

The lasers are controlled by a circuit – which is linked to a bank of explosives! What is the **FOUR-DIGIT CODE** you need to deactivate the lasers and escape? Perhaps **CONNECTING UP THE CIRCUIT BOARD** will help you?

1 2 3 4

----

1 2 3 4 5
6 7 8 9 0

CUBE MINERS

Hurtling through the portal, you arrive in a green and glowing world. The landscape is made of blocks, and so are the animals, people and monsters... in fact, everything's made of blocks!

An angular-looking pig stares at you in surprise. "What strange, squishy creatures you are! You'll need to solve four puzzles to escape this level," he snorts. "Good luck!"

A pile of **CUBES AND CUBOIDS** starts to shuffle around, rearranging constantly into **DIFFERENT PATTERNS**. You think they want to tell you something, but what?

A screen pops up in front of you, showing the following symbols:

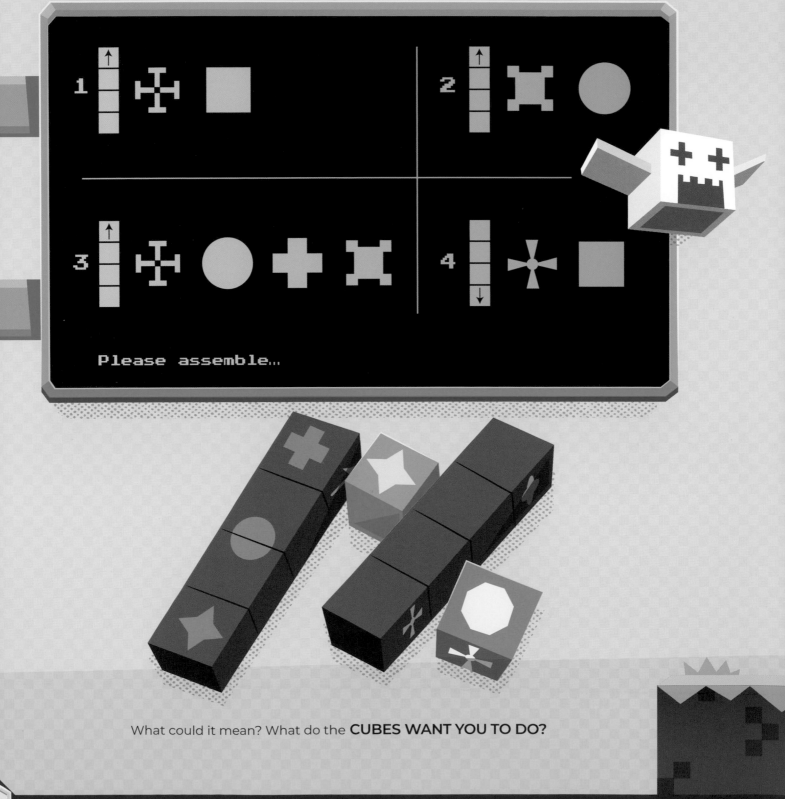

What could it mean? What do the **CUBES WANT YOU TO DO?**

To your surprise, the assembled cubes then form themselves into the shape of an old man. He points to the **REMAINS OF A TREE STUMP** on the ground, which has been cut into **FOUR EQUAL PIECES**.

"Young people," he says to you, "if you can tell me how old that tree was when it was felled, I shall help you on your quest."

Can you reassemble the tree stump and work out **HOW MANY YEARS OLD** it was?

"Not bad, youngster!" says the old man, when you give him the answer. He offers to help you further if you can help him construct a new tree.

"Trees here can be **BUILT OUT OF SIMPLE SHAPES**," he says. "Build me a tree and then tell me what **FOUR THINGS** are required in your own world for such a plant."

The old man is delighted with the **NEW TREE** you have constructed and fascinated to hear what is needed to 'build' a tree in your own world.

He hands you a **STRANGE, GOLDEN OBJECT**. "This is a powerful medal," he explains. "It will identify you as one of us **CUBE-LANDERS** and let you **PASS THROUGH A PORTAL** into the next level."

To exit, all you need to do is state your **QUALIFICATION**, which is written on the medal. What do you say?

DRAGON'S THRONE

It's the last level! As you step through the portal you shiver. An eerie breeze blows through this desolate world. You're in a huge, echoing cavern. Listening, you hear the sounds of battle all around you.

Carved into the wall are five glowing portals. Through them, you can see the levels you've defeated. The sixth portal is much bigger than the others – but it is closed.

An immense dragon lies across it, next to a giant throne. He rears his head. "Almost there, adventurers," he growls. "Solve the last four puzzles... and the portal to your world will open."

As you approach the dragon, he lazily moves aside to reveal an arrangement of **LARGE METAL CIRCLES** in the floor.

You discover that you can rotate them. Perhaps there is a particular way to arrange them that will make sense and **OPEN THE FINAL PORTAL**?

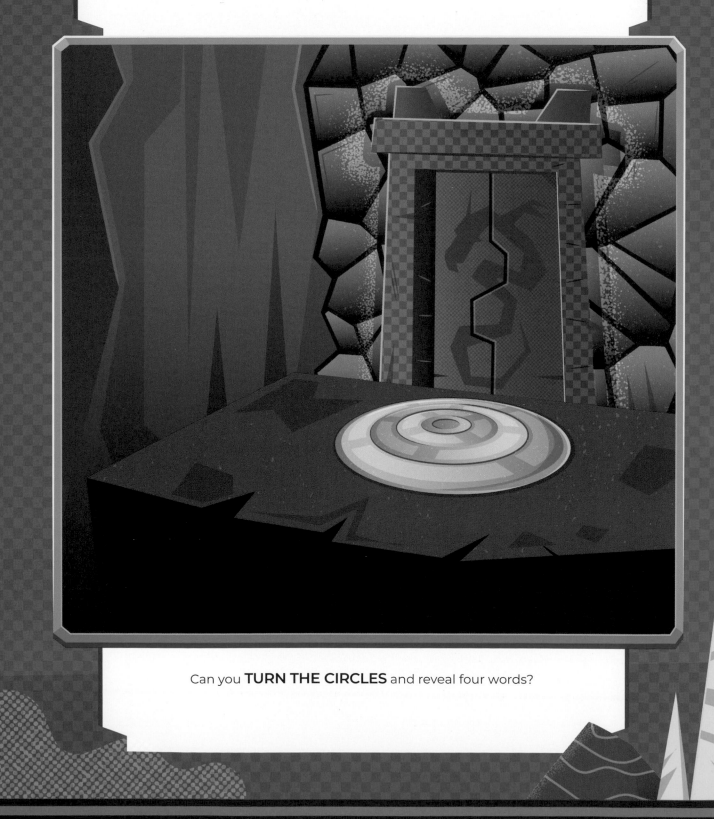

Can you **TURN THE CIRCLES** and reveal four words?

You reveal the words, but the portal doesn't open. Instead, the circles start to revolve to reveal a **HIDDEN CHAMBER** in the centre. Inside is a pile of **12 FLAT DIAMOND PIECES**.

You spot an inscription inside the chamber. "**SPEAK THREE WORDS**," it reads. Perhaps if you rearrange these diamonds, they can help you **REVEAL THE SPELL?**

The portal starts to glow, but it still doesn't open. You head towards the dragon, and he looks up at you again – and laughs. "**STILL TWO TO GO, MORTAL**."

The dragon gestures with his head, and suddenly what looks like a **MAGIC WAND** appears at your feet, accompanied by a long and narrow piece of parchment.

What two-word message does the magic wand reveal?

"Heed my warning!" laughs the dragon, amused at what you have just revealed. He raises a huge foreleg and pulls off a **GLEAMING SILVER BAND** with his teeth. He throws it down in front of you, where it shatters into pieces.

"To complete your task," he growls, "you must restore my magic band and tell me **WHAT IT IS THAT I GUARD**."

FINAL BOSS!

As you solve the last puzzle, the final portal opens. Through its swirling vortex, you can see your **LIVING ROOM**. It's the way out! You go to step through it... but are stopped by a **GIGANTIC CLAW**.

The dragon laughs, with a sound like thunder. "**FOOLS!**" he says. "I called this game to unlock the **PORTAL TO YOUR WORLD** for me. Within minutes, the portal will be large enough for me to travel through.
Then I will **LAY WASTE TO YOUR WORLD**... and you will never escape this game!"

You rack your brains. There must be a way to **STOP THIS CREATURE**.

"Nobody can defeat me!" roars the dragon. "The only word that can destroy me is engraved on **SIX CRYSTAL GEMS** – and I have **HIDDEN THEM ALL**, one on every level!"

"Quick," you say. "There's still time. Let's jump back into the other levels and find those gems!"

Can you spot the hidden gems in every level? Each one of the gems has a **DIFFERENT LETTER** on it.

Having found the gems, you return to the Dragon's Throne. You rearrange them into a word, and suddenly a **STONE TABLET RISES UP**, engraved with the words of a powerful spell. You **SPEAK THE RHYMING SPELL** engraved on the stone:

Turn fire to stone and save the player,
Make me now the dragon _ _ _ _ _ _ !

The dragon lunges at you – but before he can attack, there is a **BLINDING FLASH OF LIGHT**. As your vision clears, you see that the dragon is standing immobile. He has been turned to stone!

Characters from every level pour through the portals. "You've done it!" they cheer. "You've destroyed the dragon and **COMPLETED THE GAME!**"

"WELL DONE, ADVENTURERS! YOU CAN FINALLY ESCAPE THE VIDEO GAME!"

ANSWERS

Page 10: Place the five jigsaw pieces into the grid. The green squares create the shapes of different digits. The solution is 5712.

Page 11: Assemble the upper floor of the maze and place it on the page as described in hint 2. The coloured legs should match with each corner of the maze in the book. Solve the maze by travelling back and forth between the two levels, travelling up to the top floor via column 2 and returning via column 3. The 2-digit code is 23:

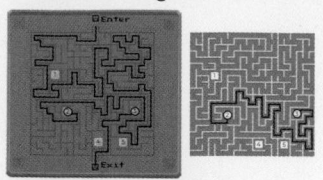

Page 12: This is the route through the maze:

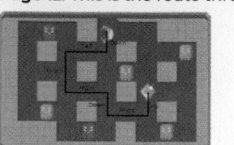

You change direction seven times. For each change of direction, lay the manic muncher over a yellow circle beneath the puzzle, facing the direction it needs to go. This will leave a letter visible. These seven letters spell POWER UP.

Page 13: Assemble the 3D maze cube shown in the picture, then find the route from START to EXIT – there is only one! Ignoring any dead ends, the path will travel over nine letters, which spell LABYRINTH:

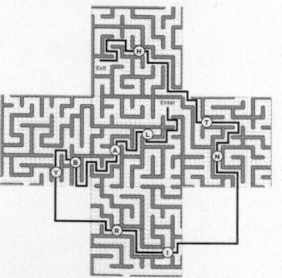

Page 16: Place four more platforms and four more ladders as follows:

Page 17: The telescope piece has images of the characters from page 17 on it. When it is assembled and placed over some of the yellow grid squares, with the black end touching the page, part of the illustration joins with the shapes on the inside of the telescope to create either an X or a tick.

Each creature reveals a symbol. The first two each reveal an X, so should be avoided, while the third is marked with a tick:

Page 18: Overlay the piece that matches the colour and design of the pixels on the display so that the colours match and the piece is centred. It then reveals the actual score of 3495.

Page 19: Find the five pieces that match the pixel design of the image, and then place them in suitable locations on top of the image to create the matching image. The solution is as follows:

Step 1 ... Step 2
Step 3 ... Step 4
Step 5

Page 22: Fold the map back and forth along the crease lines to match the picture shown on the page. Then, viewing it side on, squeeze the surfaces labelled A (below) together, and look at the top of the map. You will see a number 2. Then squeeze the B surfaces together, to reveal 4, and finally the C surfaces together to reveal 7.

The numbers will appear like this:

Page 23: Find the similar-looking octagonal piece and align it over the octagonal drawing. Then rotate it until the black shape matches the design of the first of the four shapes shown at the top of the page. The arrow on the octagonal piece will be pointing at one of the eight buttons. This is the first button to press. Repeat for the other three shapes to give the answer:

Page 24: Find the four scraps of parchment, then fold the scrap with the first symbol above the door marked on it. Once fully folded, the parchment creates the shape of a number. This is the first digit for the keypad. Next, fold each of the other three scraps, in the order shown by the symbols, to reveal the next three digits: 3014.

Page 25: First, fold and assemble the altar, so the letters are on the outside. Next, fold down the four sides of the altar cloth, and hang it over the altar, so the holes on the top of it align with the marks on the altar. You can now read a word on each side of the covered altar: THE PASSWORD IS WATERFALL.

Page 28: Find the two pieces with parts of the rings printed on them. You can insert one piece into the other by sliding half of one piece into half of the other, so they look like this image on the right:

If you then fold them flat, you can rotate one piece around the other to create a variety of ring patterns. You can also turn over one or both of the pieces, to create other arrangements. By doing this, you can create the five ring patterns shown. Each ring pattern will then reveal a number in the centre of the ring, so the solution is 74089:

Page 29: Find the four electronic component pieces and assemble them in the order and orientation shown in the circuit, so the end of one piece slots into the start of the next, to form a square. Read around the outside of the circuit from the '+' of the battery to the '-' to reveal: LIGHT UP THE WORLD.

Page 30: Assemble the three buildings then arrange them as shown in the leftmost arrangement on the page, taking care that the circular yellow roof vents on top match the exact positions shown in the picture. Then look at them from the direction shown by the arrow, making sure your eyeline is as close to the level of the buildings as possible. You will see that the lights on their sides form the number 4. Then repeat with each of the three other building arrangements, to find three more numbers. The solution is 4295:

Page 31: Find the four pieces that match the colours of the terminals on the circuit board. Place them on to the circuit in the order shown by the circles beneath the board, from left to right. Make sure the white-circled end goes on the white terminal, and the black-circled end goes on the black terminal. This then leaves four numbers visible. Reading from top to bottom, left to right gives 7429:

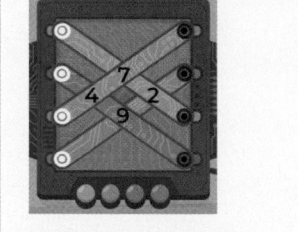

Page 34: Assemble the two cubes and two cuboids shown on the page. Starting with set 1 on the screen, place the cuboid with the arrow on it so that the orientation of the arrow matches the image on the screen. Next, arrange the other pieces so that the faces marked with the other symbols in the set touch one another. This will be easier if you lay the cuboid with the arrow flat on a surface, so you can rest the cubes next to it. This makes the shape of a letter C. Now repeat with the other three sets of symbols to reveal three more letters. Not all the pieces will be used for every letter. The answer is CHAT:

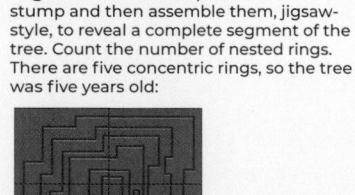

Page 35: Find the four parts of the tree stump and then assemble them, jigsaw-style, to reveal a complete segment of the tree. Count the number of nested rings. There are five concentric rings, so the tree was five years old:

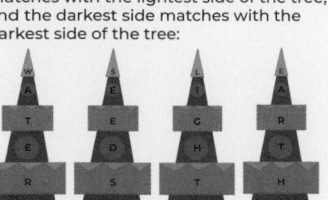

Page 36: Build the shapes shown in the illustration, then arrange them to form a tree as shown below. Make sure that each piece is rotated so that the lightest side matches with the lightest side of the tree, and the darkest side matches with the darkest side of the tree:

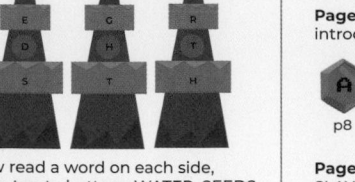

You can now read a word on each side, reading from top to bottom: WATER, SEEDS, LIGHT and EARTH.

Page 37: Find the piece that matches the item shown in the picture. Fold the sticking-out parts so that the bright yellow parts are all on the same side, and the dark yellow parts are all on the same side.

Read clockwise around each side, starting from the bold letter. Your qualification is: MINING EXPERT.

Page 40: Press out the three rings and the circle shown in the illustration, and arrange them so that you can read four words. Each word reads out from the central O in a straight line: ONCE, OPEN, OPAL and OURS.

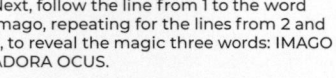

Page 41: Find the 12 pieces shown in the illustration, and assemble them so that all of the line segments join together:

Next, follow the line from 1 to the word imago, repeating for the lines from 2 and 3, to reveal the magic three words: IMAGO ADORA OCUS.

Page 42: Fold the magic wand to match the picture on the page, and find the strip of parchment. Wrap the parchment around the wand so that each end aligns with the yellow strips at either end of the wand. The slits in the wand will help you. Now, look side-on at the wand and read alternating letters from either side of the strip by looking through the windows cut in the wand. This will reveal the word DRAGON on one side and BEWARE on the other:

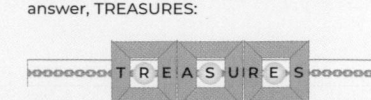

Page 43: Find, fold and assemble three jewels to match the picture. Next, find the piece that matches the silver band shown in the image, and slide the jewels on to the band so that, from left to right, they are purple, green and red. Make sure that you can see through the hole on one side of each jewel to the letters on the band beneath.

Next, you will need to make sure the jewels are rotated so that all the letters face the same way. Finally, once the jewels are all centred over letters, you can reveal the final answer, TREASURES:

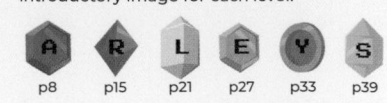

Page 45: One gem is hidden in the introductory image for each level.

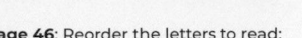

p8   p15   p21   p27   p33   p39

Page 46: Reorder the letters to read: SLAYER.